Write Here, Write Now

A collection of children's writing
from the 2002 awards.

Hodder & Stoughton

A MEMBER OF THE HODDER HEADLINE GROUP

Orders: please contact Bookpoint Ltd, 130 Milton Park, Abingdon, Oxon
OX14 4SB. Telephone: (44) 01235 827720. Fax: (44) 01235 400454. Lines
are open from 9.00–6.00, Monday to Saturday, with a 24 hour message
answering service. You can also order through our website
www.madaboutbooks.com.

British Library Cataloguing in Publication Data
A catalogue record for this title is available from the British Library

ISBN 0 340 858702

First Published 2002
Impression number   10 9 8 7 6 5 4 3 2 1
Year   2007 2006 2005 2004 2003 2002

Typeset by Fakenham Photosetting Limited, Fakenham, Norfolk.
Printed in Great Britain for Hodder & Stoughton Educational, a division of
Hodder Headline Ltd, 338 Euston Road, London NW1 3BH by Cox &
Wyman.

Write Here, Write Now

CONTENTS

Foreword by Stephen Twigg, MP · vii
Introduction · viii

POEM · 1
John Hegley wrote... · 3
INTRODUCTION · 4
Anger · 7
Smelly Socks · 8
The Thing Is · 9
The Fox Who Threatens Night · 10
The Thing Is... · 12
The Thing Is · 14
The Rats · 16
My Secret Rock · 17
My Head of Secrets · 18
My Sweet Little Pet Did It! · 20
The Thing Is · 22
Hoverbikes Are Go · 24

PERSUASIVE WRITING · 27
Terry Jones wrote... · 29
INTRODUCTION · 30
Why Living in the Country is Better than
   Living in the City · 33
The Town is the Place to Be! · 35
Countryside v Townies in the Cup Final · 37
Town or Country? · 39
Come and Live in the Countryside · 41
Country vs. City · 43
Town or Country? · 45
The Town · 47
All for Countryside! · 49
Town versus Country · 51

STORY   **53**
Jacqueline Wilson wrote...   55
INTRODUCTION   56
Wild Memories   59
Guilty!   62
The Cannibal   65
The Ghost Catcher   68
Escape!   70
"You Can Run but you Can't Hide"   73
Not for the Faint-Hearted   76
Curse of Darkness   79
Gangster Trouble   81
The Ghost Baby   84
The Bullies   87

JOURNALISM   **91**
Lizo Mzimba wrote...   93
INTRODUCTION   94
FOREST TOWN NEWS   97
School News   98
MYSTERY BUG EMPTIES SCHOOL   100
KILLER BEES INVADE SCHOOL   102
WATERLOGGED ST WINEFRIDE'S!   104
TEACHER SHOCK   106
TWO TREES TERRORISE!   108
Doulwood Express   109
PANTHER COMES FOR LESSONS
  – SPOTTED BY BECKHAM   110

Bullying – how to deal with it   **112**

FOREWORD

Stephen Twigg, MP
Parliamentary Under-Secretary of State for
Young People and Learning

The Write Here, Write Now writing awards support the National Literacy Strategy. The Literacy Strategy has earned widespread support from teachers and is helping to improve standards of reading and writing in primary schools, and providing children with the skills they need to enhance their creativity and exercise their imagination.

Write Here, Write Now 2002 has been a great success. We received over 20,000 entries from budding authors throughout England. We were, of course, looking for evidence of good spelling, punctuation and grammar, but we also wanted to see children applying their imagination and producing work that was inventive and original. I hope all the children taking part, and not just the winners, found it interesting and exciting.

I am very grateful to everyone involved in Write Here, Write Now, particularly the children for all their hard work and the teachers who guided and supported them. I would like to thank the judges who had the enjoyable task of reading all the entries. I would also like to thank the BBC, Hodder and Stoughton, Dell and Mindscape, who made such a valuable contribution by sponsoring the prizes.

I am grateful to John Hegley, Terry Jones, Lizo Mzimba and Jacqueline Wilson who, with their opening lines, provided the inspiration for the children and stimulated such high quality work. I enjoyed reading the imaginative ways in which children developed their pieces of writing.

We want all children to develop their literacy skills and to enjoy writing. The National Literacy Strategy is helping and these awards are an important way of supporting improvements in writing. I hope this brilliant collection of children's writing encourages other children to be creative.

I hope everyone who reads this book finds it inspiring and entertaining.

INTRODUCTION

Once again, the Write Here, Write Now writing awards have been a huge success, inspiring thousands of children in Years 4 and 5 (ages 8–10).

As entries for the 2002 awards poured in from all over the country, the regional judging panels realised what a hard task lay ahead of them. Many of the entries were of an exceptionally high quality – lively, challenging and, above all, written with enormous enthusiasm.

There were four categories of writing for the children to choose from – Poem, Persuasive Writing, Story and, for group entries, Journalism. Each category had a stimulus piece written by a leading figure in their field. **John Hegley** provided a mysterious verse with endless possibilities. **Terry Jones** wrote a challenging – and topical – essay on the merits of the town versus the country. **Jacqueline Wilson's** opener was urgent and sinister, allowing the children to use their imaginations freely, while **Lizo Mzimba** invited the writers to create a carefully edited piece of journalism.

All the entries in this book are regional winners, and as you will see they are a mixture of the comic, the serious, the lyrical and the hard-edged. Each category has an overall national winner, selected by a celebrity judging panel after many hours of lively discussion. There are also several awards for improvement, written by children who were nominated by their teachers for showing significant progress in their writing and general literacy skills.

The children's work has been edited only lightly, to allow their individual styles and voices to shine through. The children's ages were correct at the time of writing.

POEM

John Hegley wrote...

The Thing Is

There's something that I haven't said
that I would like to say,
the thing I'm thinking in my head
that I've kept kept away.
I've had it hidden really well
but now I want to share
my secret with you, yes I do,
I want to, and I dare...

INTRODUCING THE POEMS

John Hegley's opening stanza could hardly be more mysterious. It's a perfect opener as it lets the imagination run wild and allows for the exploration of a range of styles, subjects and emotions.

Timothy Martin Wood has used the poem to explore pent-up anger and frustration. His use of powerful images – "I feel like a tiger striking its prey" – and strong words gives us a sense of the speaker's overwhelming rage. In contrast, **Emma Hodgson's** interpretation is an hilarious ode to smelly socks, with the added twist of the reason why the socks are never taken off.

Jamie Hartley continues the sense of mystery by never quite revealing his secret, despite tantalising us with wonderful metaphors of the deep ocean. **Ross Payne's** poem has a Gothic feel and evocative use of phrases which conjure up the dark, menacing world of the "fox who threatens night".

Grace Machon leaves us guessing until the very end in her beautifully imagined verses, each one of which is a riddle in itself. **Hannah Bentley's** poem is song-like and catchy – she manages to keep her secret, leaving us dying to know what it is!

Animals feature again in **Daniel Towns'** celebration of rats, which conjures up wonderful images of dancing rodents and ends with a crushing blow to all things feline. **Ross O'Neill** combines heroic and fantastic images to conjure up a dramatic history for his secret, while **Theo Hopkinson's** poem is a wistful description of friendship. **Helena Redman's** story will be familiar to everyone who has ever been in the wrong — and tried to get away with it. Her choice of language, especially at the end of her poem, accurately reflects those familiar excuses.

Oscar Kirby-Hogarty provides us with a searing exploration of loneliness and loss. His description of happy memories will touch everyone who reads it deeply. Finally, **Leo Portal** reveals the secret world of the child super-hero, whose heroic deeds will save the world.

As you will see, each poem is unique and leaves lasting images in your mind. Be prepared to move swiftly from laughter to tears and from suspense to comic-book heroics — the power of poetry is clearly evident in these pages.

Anger

There's something that I haven't said
That I would like to say,
The thing I'm thinking in my head
That I've kept kept away.
I've had it hidden really well
But now I want to share
My secret with you, yes I do,
I want to and I dare...

When anger strikes over me,
I feel like a thousand bolts of
lightning charging through my body,
I feel like a tiger striking its prey.
It's like Satan dribbling up into my mind.
I feel like I want to destroy.

I feel like the good has been drained
out of me
And evil has rained upon me.
The heat of anger circles around me,
and I start to bubble up into pain.
It makes me feel like I want to thump,
smack, swear, throw, break.
If I don't let the anger out soon, I
will start to fight.
Too late, I explode, anger replaced by
sadness.

By Timothy Martin Wood, aged 9
Bradley CofE Primary School

 EAST MIDLANDS WINNER

Smelly Socks

There's something that I haven't said
That I would like to say,
The thing I'm thinking in my head
That I've kept kept away.

I've had it hidden really well
But now I want to share
My secret with you, yes I do,
I want to and I dare...

These ordinary socks,
I wear them every day.
They may be pretty smelly,
But listen to what I say.

The reason that I wear them,
And they're not in the bin,
Because they are the only socks
Which fit seven toes in!

The reason I have seven toes
I just don't have a clue.
But that's my secret said and done,
And nobody knows but you.

Can I trust you with my secret?
Will you please not tell a soul?
'Cause on these feet, my seven toes,
They're rare, they're me, they make me whole!

By Emma Hodgson, aged 9
St Luke's CofE Primary School

LONDON WINNER

The Thing Is

There's something that I haven't said
that I would like to say,
the thing I'm thinking in my head
that I've kept kept away.
I've had it hidden really well
But now I want to share
My secret with you, yes I do,
I want to, and I dare...
A secret is like a pearl in the ocean
Deep in the sand
Locked up in a clam
So you still want to know? Hmm
You must be very brave
You'd have to be brave to know
The man-eating sharks
Circling above the precious pearl
Dive deep deep down
It gets colder and darker
How long will it take to get there?
It just wants to be told
It is growing on me.

By Jamie Hartley, aged 10
St Winifride's RC Primary School

AWARDS FOR IMPROVEMENT JOINT WINNER

The Fox who Threatens Night

There's something that I haven't said
that I would like to say,
the thing I'm thinking in my head
that I've kept kept away.
I've had it hidden really well
But now I want to share
My secret with you, yes I do,
I want to, and I dare...

Deep in the forest, by this town,
Inside its darkened den,
A fox, with fur as black as night,
Longs for a feast of men.

Now years ago, I met this fox,
Surprised to hear it talk,
It asked me to catch it food that either
Swims or flies or walks.

And ever since, I've killed wildlife,
But not for fun or feast,
But for the fox who threatens night,
That heartless, slavering beast.

And now it wants to make me kill
The townsfolk of this city,
His shadowy mind cares only for himself,
On others he has no pity.

That is the secret I have kept,
Spread it through the people,
To get that evil fox caught and shot
And thrown down from the steeple.

We'll feed his body to our dogs,
Our dogs of speed and might,
We'll rid this threat for all mankind,
The fox who threatens night.

By Ross Payne, aged 10
Elsworth CofE Primary School

EAST OF ENGLAND WINNER

The Thing Is...

There's something that I haven't said
that I would like to say,
the thing I'm thinking in my head
that I've kept kept away.
I've had it hidden really well
But now I want to share
My secret with you, yes I do,
I want to, and I dare...

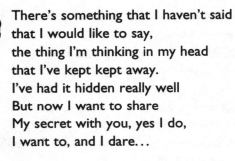

My secret is that
I've fallen in love
The girl I've fallen in love with
Has a long green dress
And a purple bonnet that covers her hair and face
Every day she dances in the wind
Her name is Tulip.

My secret is that
I've fallen in love
The girl I've fallen in love with
Is an extremely tall true English girl
Scarlet is her hair
She is a favourite of mine
Her name is Rose.

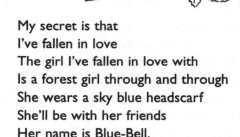

My secret is that
I've fallen in love
The girl I've fallen in love with
Is a forest girl through and through
She wears a sky blue headscarf
She'll be with her friends
Her name is Blue-Bell.

I love them all as they live in my garden
I'm their tender and carer
I am a gardener
They are my flowers
My pride, my joy, my secret world.

By Grace Machon, aged 10
Stramongate Primary School

NORTH WEST WINNER

The Thing Is

There's something that I haven't said,
That I would like to say,
The thing I'm thinking in my head,
That I've kept kept away.

I've had it hidden really well,
But now I want to share
My secret with you, yes I do,
I want to and I dare.

I need to tell you now,
I swore I wouldn't say,
I really don't know how
My life got blown away.

You see the problem is,
I beg you, please don't shout,
I've got to let it go,
I've got to let it out.

Can't keep it to myself,
Can't keep it in my head,
Can't keep it any longer,
Can't sleep when I'm in bed.

I don't know how to say it,
I can't explain it well,
I have to tell somebody,
I really need to tell.

I can't think how I kept it,
I don't know how I did,
The thing I'm thinking in my head,
I don't know how it hid.

I think I have achieved
The skill I always wanted,
To keep a secret safe and sound,
And never to be taunted.

By Hannah Bentley, aged 9
St Mary's Middle School

SOUTH WEST WINNER

The Rats

There's something that I haven't said
that I would like to say,
the thing I'm thinking in my head
that I've kept kept away.
I've had it hidden really well
but now I want to share
my secret with you, yes I do,
I want to and I dare...

It's the rats.

I live with rats, I swim with rats,
I dance with rats, I sing with rats,
I chant with rats, I eat with rats,
I walk and talk and read with rats.

I've kept it secret from you all
because you'll say: "You stink.
The stupid ugly hairy things
are even in your sink."

I know you're not that passionate
about these hairy rats
but I'm a friend to all of them
and I despise your cats.

By Daniel Towns, aged 9, St Godric's RC Primary School

**NORTH EAST WINNER
NATIONAL WINNER**

16

My Secret Rock

There's something that I haven't said
that I would like to say,
the thing I'm thinking in my head
that I've kept kept away.
I've had it hidden really well
but now I want to share
my secret with you, yes I do,
I want to and I dare....

My secret is a rock but not
any rock.
A dazzling flashy, amber
crystal rock.
I still think where it came
from, what time,
maybe an atom from the
dinosaur age,
Or a knight in shining armour
found it in a dragon's cave.
But wherever it came from
it is mine.

By Ross O'Neill, aged 10
Hook Junior School

AWARDS FOR IMPROVEMENT JOINT WINNER

My Head of Secrets

There's something that I haven't said
That I would like to say,
The thing that I'm thinking in my head
That I've kept kept away.
I've had it hidden really well
But now I want to share
My secret with you, yes I do,
I want to and I dare.

My head is like a grimy prison,
A cell without a door.
My feelings come out mingled and muddled,
I'm not someone any more.

My secrets and my treasures
I share to you with pride.
Although they're small and boring,
Not once or twice I've lied.

Maybe they do make sense to you,
Or maybe then they don't.
I'll never know, I'll never know,
I won't, I won't, I won't.

The wind runs more freely
Than I will ever run,
The clouds are like my brainwaves,
Blocking up the sun.

Maybe you'll remember me, one day,
As a joyful happy lad,
You'll think of me, us old mates true,
And think of the fun we had.

By Theo Hopkinson, aged 10
Thames Ditton Junior School

  SOUTH EAST WINNER

My Sweet Little Pet Did It!

There's something that I haven't said
that I would like to say,
the thing I'm thinking in my head
that I've kept kept away.
I've had it hidden really well
but now I want to share
my secret with you, yes I do,
I want to, and I dare...

You see – I – well – it goes like
    this, the writing on my door,
you know I said it was Edward, I don't think that any more.
It's kinda hard to tell you this, I don't know what to say,
please please pretty please don't get cross – it was yonks
    ago, anyway!

Well, I had Edward round for tea (that's the bit you know),
this might get me in your bad books, but I don't care much,
    soooo...
I'll tell you all the story, beginning to the end,
some bits are pretty gory – I don't mean to offend!

I *know* you hate that kind of thing! Er – is it better to save it
    for now?
No? OK then, here it is, you can't stop me, anyhow!
We played a game, just me and Ed (it was a game of dares),
"I dare you to draw on the door," Ed said. Don't reckon he
    really cares!

Well anyway, I took my pen, was just about to draw,
but it was just too naughty! To draw on my bedroom door!
Eddie called me a chicken. Well, we'll see about that!
He was the chicken soon enough, the little scaredy cat!

I know what you're thinking. You're just wondering why,
why I called Ed a scaredy cat. He couldn't believe his eyes!
Coming out of my cupboard door, a purple hairy hand!
You should've heard him scream, man! Prob'ly shook half
    the land!

My pet emerged from the cupboard, a monster, 'twas, indeed,
I'd kept him since I was *so small*! When I found this monster,
    in need.
I felt so sorry for him though, so home he came with me.
He's lived in my cupboard ever since, fed on leftovers
    from tea!

Anyway, back to the story now. I handed him my pen,
He doodled away on the door, soooooooo I covered it up
with a poster!

By the way, my monster has run away now,
so I can't really prove that he did it and...
oh, alright.

    It was me.

By Helena Redman, aged 10
Christ Church Primary School

    WEST MIDLANDS WINNER

21

The Thing Is

There's something that I haven't said
that I would like to say,
the thing I'm thinking in my head
that I've kept kept away.
I've had it hidden really well
but now I want to share
my secret with you, yes I do,
I want to, and I dare...

Although I seem a happy boy
I'm hurt deep down inside,
I never had a single toy
a thing I've tried to hide.
I never saw my mum or dad,
how much I've cried and cried,
I really hate being in this home,
I wish they never died...

Now I'm frightened of fast cars
I'm terrified of crashes,
this is how they reached the stars
and how they turned to ashes.
I'm trying to hide the fact I know
I'll always be alone,
I laugh and joke and fool around
so my feelings won't be known...

I close my eyes and then I stare,
I see them holding me,
they smile with love and deepest care,
    from all my hurt I'm free.
Although my mum and dad are dead,
    their images keep me strong,
that's why my secret's been so safe
    ... I've hidden it so long.

By Oscar Kirby-Hogarty, aged 9
Stanley Junior School

    AWARDS FOR IMPROVEMENT JOINT WINNER

Hoverbikes Are Go

There's something that I haven't said
That I would like to say,
The thing I'm thinking in my head
That I've kept kept away.
I've had it hidden really well
But now I want to share
My secret with you, yes I do,
I want to and I dare...

I am a superhero
And my cousin Edward too
Spend any time with me, oh
What things you'll have to do.
Using our fast hoverbikes
We speed to danger zone
We rescue people quickly
And they never make a moan.

We rescue them in outer space
From black holes and pulsars,
We pull them from the planet's face
And pass the burning stars.
We adventure underwater
From squid and great white shark,
We put a light on just in case
We enter somewhere dark.

Don't forget the alligators
That lurk in bubbling swamp,
It was the prey the reptile tore –
We arrived there with some pomp.
The baking city getting hot
From burning lava flows
With magma flowing up the vent
Of a row of volcanoes.

The rumbling of the earthquake
But nobody will worry
For we are superheroes
And we'll get there in a hurry.

By Leo Portal, aged 10
Birstwith CofE Primary School

   YORKSHIRE AND HUMBERSIDE WINNER

PERSUASIVE WRITING

Terry Jones wrote...

The real problem with living in the country is that there are far more sheep than people. Not that I've got anything against sheep, but you try inviting a couple round for dinner and you'll soon find out the problems. For example, sheep never have enough money for a cab home and you always end up either driving them yourself or else having to pay for a cab for them. Then again it's so noisy in the country. Just try to sleep with all those owls hooting, foxes howling, dogs barking, cows mooing and sheep bleating ... not to mention the rats scampering in the wainscotting and the cat knocking over saucepan racks as it pounces on some squeaking rodent. But worst of all is the weather. You get it in the country. You don't in town. In town we are blissfully unaware whether the sun is shining, whether it's raining, whether it's hot or cold, whether it's day or night. We can get on with our work and we're not dominated every living minute of the day by what the sky's doing. No, give me the town – any town – every town – rather than a load of fields.

INTRODUCING THE PERSUASIVE WRITING

Have *you* ever invited a sheep round for dinner? If so, you'll understand why **Terry Jones** is so unimpressed by the countryside. His provocative piece inspired a huge number of entries singing the praises of both town and country in a variety of ways – hilarious, passionate and metaphorical.

Pico Manocci, Edward Seater, Joanna Clifford, Max Carrington and **Olivia Burton** set out to prove Terry wrong. In their opinion, the country is far superior to the stuffy old town with its stressful pace of life and pollution. Activities such as riding, fishing or simply listening to the animals and birds offer peaceful ways to pass the day, while for many of the writers big gardens, fields and open spaces are a huge benefit. Low crime levels in the country are also an important factor, as is the lack of traffic jams. While Terry sees the weather in the country as a problem, our countryside fans see it as a celebration of the natural world around them.

For **Nikhit Guntupalli, Emily Curtin, Molly Cox, Ben Scott** and **Emma Woods** the town is the place to be! Only in the town can you "have a haircut on a regular basis," see the latest cinema blockbusters or classic pantos, have a social life and go shopping. The smell of manure causes deep concern to many of our townies! Ants, wasps, angry old grannies and other hidden dangers lurk everywhere in the countryside, while the silence and darkness are scary or irritating. Buses, taxis, a variety of work places, schools and colleges and quick access to the emergency services make the town much more appealing in these writers' eyes.

Terry Jones certainly picked a subject which provoked strong views and some powerful writing.

Why Living in the Country is Better than Living in the City

Some people may argue that living in the city is better than living in the country, but I personally think that the city is polluted, stuffy, crowded and claustrophobic.

For example, some people get terrible asthma in the city, caused by pollution as a result of all the cars.

The city may offer things like cafés and cinemas, but not horse riding and fishing and a range of other outdoor activities.

The city is stressful and over-powering. Some people do yoga to release their stress, but all the stress just comes back in two hours! Working in the city is long and tiring, due to the tremendous amount of work employees have to do.

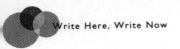

On the other hand, the country is peaceful, quiet and organic.

Some people think that you're more likely to get hay fever in the country, but you're just as likely to get it in the city and only 10% suffer from hay fever.

The country provides organic and free-range food and spacious housing, backed up with a big garden, and if the garden isn't big enough, you can always roam around the fields.

You may have to commute two hours in order to get to work, but you can just look forward to coming home to your beautiful manor or cottage in the countryside, and having a nice organic meal to end the day.

I think I have persuaded, without a doubt, that living in the country is better by far than living in the city.

By Pico Manocci, aged 10
Barrow Hill Junior School

 AWARDS FOR IMPROVEMENT JOINT WINNER

The Town is the Place to Be!

What's so good about living in the country?! In the town you can have a haircut on a regular basis and obviously you won't look like a silly 60's popstar. I can assure you that you won't look good if you don't have a decent haircut and you end up looking like a sheared sheep!

Fortunately, in towns there are cinemas and of course theatres. In cinemas you can see the latest box office blockbusters on a big screen with Dolby Digital 5.1 and see films like "Scooby Doo". Alternatively, if you like old fashioned plays, you can go to the theatre where you can see famous pantomimes like "Dick Whittington". I like to see men who dress like women. What a laugh they are. You see plenty of these in a town!

Lovely smells! How nice they are compared to the smell of ... horse manure! I really do think the air freshening in the country is a real problem! Can you imagine that?! But in the town, oh, what good smells – smells of pizza restaurants. Say, how many times have you seen a child literally dragging their family along to have a burger?! But still the town is the core of an apple!

The towns also have interesting places like museums rather than a place full of grass to shear! Continuing with the grass problem we townies use modern technology to cut grass. We use a mower not shears which make your arms ache a lot and your hand sore.

In the town, there are millions and millions of people so you never are alone, but in the country, huh, all you do is feed the cattle and cut the crops and at 10 o'clock, watch the news. Yawn!! With lots of people in the town you can make friends so easily and quickly and you never ever will be alone.

Finally, it's more fun in the town. You can go to Playzone, Woodcocks – what fun they are compared to the country. There are discos too, groovy!

Just give me a town, whether a poor town or a rich town – just give me a town rather than farmers who look like silly 60's hippies!

By Nikhit Guntupalli, aged 10
Westgate Junior School

 EAST MIDLANDS WINNER

Countryside v Townies in the Cup Final

The match is about to start. It's the Countryside v the Townies. Who will win this terrific game? Will it be the Countryside or the Townies? Manager for the Countryside is Willy Willow, and manager for the Townies is Rufuss Road. And the Ref is going to blow his whistle, *whhhh* and the game begins.

Have you ever sat outside on a glorious summer's evening listening to the animals singing and talking? It's very relaxing – you can almost fall asleep and be part of the countryside. On the other hand, the town has got noises, lots of noises, but they are cars and trucks. It's not very peaceful, is it?

Furthermore, in the town you don't get very big gardens. You might get big gardens but often they are small. Sometimes you get yards with nothing in except a

washing-line and a few plant pots, but some yards can be very pretty with plants and decking. However in the countryside you get big gardens and woods surrounding fields and lush green grass.

In addition, in the town there are rows of houses and flats and buildings. You get dark alleyways with graffiti and junk. It's not a very pretty place to live. Admittedly some parts of the town are pretty, but not as pretty as the countryside.

In the town the crime rates are high. One minute you are walking down the street then the next minute somebody jumps out of an alley with a balaclava on and your handbag gets taken. Street crimes are getting higher. In the countryside you don't get burgled. Well, yes, all right, you might get burgled a couple of times but not as much as in the town.

In the country it isn't crowded. It has a couple of cars going past your house a day. There are no traffic jams or hundreds of people walking up and down the street every day, spending their money on clothes and toys and books. The town's really very busy.

It's Grass for the Countryside. He's past the Townies' defender, he shoots and scooooores! What a goal! Top corner! He dribbled round the defender, shot and scored. *Whhhh* and there goes the final whistle of this exciting game. Countryside wins the cup.

By Edward Seater, aged 10
Streatley CofE Primary School

   SOUTH EAST WINNER

Town or Country?

I would so prefer to live in the town; I mean, who wants to live in the countryside where there is no chance of having any kind of social life because there is nothing to do? I mean, no cinemas or shopping centres. Total disaster!

Anyway, if you did have a small shop anywhere near you it is bound to be shut down because it has hardly any business. This is because there are only about three houses living within ten miles! When you are in desperate need of doing something like going to the cinema or shopping then it takes you absolutely ages and ages to get there.

Also, when you walk out of your front door you have to run back inside with your hand covering your mouth or you will be poisoned by the smell of cow pat and manure!

OK, so there is more wildlife but who wants sheep bleating or cows mooing and tractors going past in the middle of the night? Then just to make it worse at around five in the morning you have bells ringing; so there is no chance at all of having a good night's sleep! One good thing about being woken up at five in the morning is that you would need to get up soon anyway to make it to school on time!

If there are any houses anywhere near you then living in them are bound to be old grannies or granddads! You know how grannies are, try to say hello and you will end up hearing their whole life story, which takes about five hours! Then you get the type who, if you so much as *touch* their plants in their garden, will run outside with their stick and will start shouting at you and waving it around!

When you live in the country you see it has stopped raining so you run outside. As soon as you get out there you are caught in a thunder storm. When you are in the town you don't really notice the rain because of all the buildings, and at least there will always be something else to do inside just in case!

People say you would get more of a sun tan in the country because in the town the sun is blocked by the buildings! But, I mean, OK you might go red and burn but I don't call that a sun tan! You would get a better tan just driving to the beach from the town, which would only take about ten minutes. If you do start to sunbathe in the countryside then you will probably be lying on about ten cowpats.

I know there is less crime in the countryside, but if there were any buildings anywhere near you they would be totally covered in graffiti because there is nothing else to do!

If you are in the countryside then you might go for a picnic, but, I mean, who wants to go for a picnic when you can have a pizza? When you start to unpack your picnic, by the time you have started eating you have been attacked by wasps or your food has been taken away by ants!

By Emily Curtin, aged 10
Bedford High School

EAST OF ENGLAND WINNER

40

Come and Live in the Countryside

The real problem with living in the town is it's just not inviting. When you invite people over they always, without a doubt, bring their car. Now the cars get bored with all the waiting so you have to spend half the night phoning the RSPCGH (Royal Society for Persuading Cars to Go Home!) and then when you finally get to sleep, guess what, some stupid, crazy drunkard, who has just come out from the next door pub, smashes your window in. But I can assure you that in the country when you invite a sheep over for tea you have a great time. It is obvious Terry Jones does not live in the country, or has ever invited a sheep round for tea, as sheep are fit chaps and you can bet your bottom dollar they will walk home. If you don't believe me invite one for tea yourself!

Then it is so quiet in the country. There are no cars hooting, drunkards howling, burglar alarms beeping ... not to mention that in the country it's so fresh, with no pollution. The fresh air rubs off on people leaving a cosy community feeling and gives everybody a chance to join in everything.

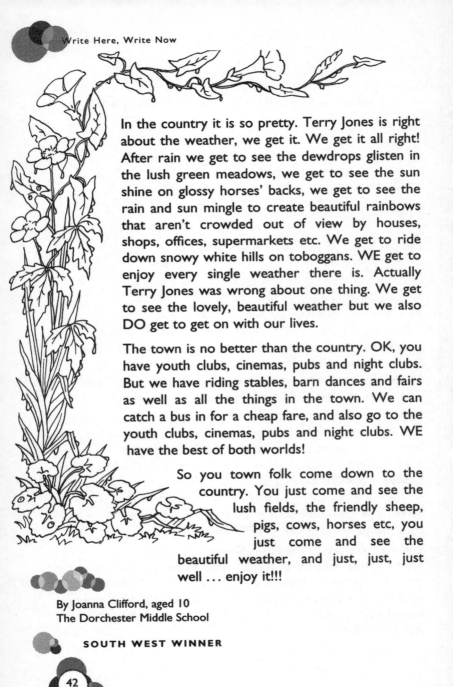

In the country it is so pretty. Terry Jones is right about the weather, we get it. We get it all right! After rain we get to see the dewdrops glisten in the lush green meadows, we get to see the sun shine on glossy horses' backs, we get to see the rain and sun mingle to create beautiful rainbows that aren't crowded out of view by houses, shops, offices, supermarkets etc. We get to ride down snowy white hills on toboggans. WE get to enjoy every single weather there is. Actually Terry Jones was wrong about one thing. We get to see the lovely, beautiful weather but we also DO get to get on with our lives.

The town is no better than the country. OK, you have youth clubs, cinemas, pubs and night clubs. But we have riding stables, barn dances and fairs as well as all the things in the town. We can catch a bus in for a cheap fare, and also go to the youth clubs, cinemas, pubs and night clubs. WE have the best of both worlds!

So you town folk come down to the country. You just come and see the lush fields, the friendly sheep, pigs, cows, horses etc, you just come and see the beautiful weather, and just, just, just well ... enjoy it!!!

By Joanna Clifford, aged 10
The Dorchester Middle School

SOUTH WEST WINNER

42

Country vs. City

I totally agree with Terry Jones because I don't like the country. I can't stand staying with my aunt and cousin, who live there, for more than three days and I don't know how they survive it.

I also agree with Terry when he says it's too noisy but I have to point out that it can also be too quiet. Sometimes there's absolutely no noise whatsoever. It's awful. You lie in bed at night and there's nothing. Whereas in the city you can guarantee that there's always going to be some noise. There are always cars zooming past and ambulance sirens whirring and eventually you get used to it.

Furthermore in the country at night it's far too dark. I mean, after all the lights have gone out and everyone's asleep it's pitch-black. Suppose you wake up in the middle of the night and decide that you need a quick drink, you'll break your leg before you get to a tap. In the city streetlights are on twenty-four hours a day. At least that's something. It's better than pitch blackness. Why don't country roads have streetlamps? It's an impossible situation!

Country roads are also too long and very windy. When you try to find an address in the country it takes a lot more time than in the city because there are very few signs. However in the city there are millions of signposts and it's very hard to get lost. Moreover if you didn't have signposts then you wouldn't know what's going on in the world. You wouldn't know that someone's cat is lost or where you can buy a second-hand computer cheaply.

Surely you can't disagree with me when I say that the smell of the country is also an extremely big problem. It stinks of manure! It's disgusting. Haven't the farmers heard of air freshener? On the other hand in the town there's the problem of pollution but after a while you get used to the smell. How could anyone ever in a million years get used to the smell of manure?

Another problem with the country is that hardly anybody lives there so if you had an accident or heart attack, you'd be dead before anybody found you, let alone phoned an ambulance. Also there are very few shops and you have to travel about three miles to get to a co-op which is usually extremely small and never has the things you need. I mean, imagine it. You wake up and decide you want a slice of toast for breakfast that morning and you get downstairs, open the bread bin and what do you find? It's totally empty. So you have to drive all the way into town to get a loaf of bread and by the time you get back it's lunchtime.

Whereas in the city there is also the problem of having too many shops and too much choice. This kind of butter or that kind of butter? This chocolate bar or that chocolate bar? It's just too tricky.

Well I think I have proved that the city is much better than the country. The country, if you think about it, is very unsafe. There should be a major redevelopment programme planned to change it so there are more lampposts and signposts, fewer noisy animals and a lot more shops selling big cans of air freshener.

By Molly Cox, aged 10
St Michael's CofE Primary School

LONDON WINNER

Town or Country?

The country – the peace, the quiet, the life. Are you bored with living a noisy life? Well, why don't you get off the cobbled concrete and onto the rich soil and live in a cottage or farm?

Pollution: Save the health of your loved ones. There are no toxic fumes in the country but there are in town. However there is nothing like the country air to flush out those bad thoughts. The country folk care about their crops, their family and they care about their lives.

Weather: Whatever the weather, wherever the weather, the weather is here, the weather is there. When it's a hot summer's day, run for shade or pick one of your beautiful fields.

Peace: Have a nap and unwind your mind in your comfy bed and be soothed to sleep by nightingales, starlings, doves, amongst other brilliant singing birds of nature.

Safety: No robbers, no convicts, no worry. If somehow something does go wrong the emergency services know where you are.

Give me the shade, give me the life, give me the country, not the dirty, dirty town. If you disagree, just think – where would we be without the country? Nowhere!

By Max Carrington, aged 10
The Sladen CofE Middle School

 WEST MIDLANDS WINNER

The Town

If I had the choice of living in either the town or the countryside, without hesitating I would know straight away which one I would prefer. The town.

It is much more exciting and enjoyable than it could ever be in the country. But what is interesting about the country? The green meadows and the empty fields? They don't sound appealing to me at all! Who would want to be swamped with insects and long, winding roads that last forever? Certainly not me!

The town has more activities and things to do. You could go bowling or swimming. Or even go to the pubs and clubs! And that isn't all: there are millions of things to do. Tell me one amusing activity you can participate in within the countryside. You may be thinking... cycling. In many towns there are specially built tracks for cyclists to ride on. Many people in the town use their bike for travelling to work. There are thousands of places to work in the town and they all require different skills. On the other hand, there are basically two jobs to do in the countryside – farming and house cleaning. How interesting!

In the town, there aren't just places of entertainment and socialising: there are lots of colleges, universities and schools. If a child or student lived in the country, the nearest place they could be educated would be approximately 7.5 miles away! And how would they get there? A taxi? In the countryside? I don't think so: taxi and cab services only run in towns and cities. A bus? Buses rarely run in the country and if by chance they do, the shortest wait for the correct bus would be at least one hour. Once again, the town has a

better service. The average bus runs every ten minutes. Eight out of ten buses depart and arrive on time.

If you wanted to go on holiday abroad, by air, and you lived in the countryside, where would the nearest airport be? In a variety of cities there are airports. That would mean trekking all the way to the city, by bus, with all your bags (unless you wanted to leave your car at the airport – assuming you had a car), then getting to the airport from the city (by taxi or even by bus – again). What a commotion! Although, who cares, you're going to have a lovely holiday – but what about when you come home?

Here's another point to prove that the town is much more appropriate than the countryside. Supposing, again, that you live in the countryside and an accident occurs. And it is an emergency. You ring for an ambulance (or a fire engine etc) and they tell you they can't come in less than half an hour, or more, because of where you live. Someone could be dead in five minutes. What do you do? Once again, if you live in the town, the ambulance etc could have reached you in less than five minutes. Or even something less serious than that. What if someone is poorly or has an infection? Where would the nearest chemist or GP be? In the town, once more.

Believe me, it is much better to live in a town than the country.

By Ben Scott, aged 10
English Martyrs' RC Primary School

NORTH EAST WINNER

48

All for Countryside!

To begin my argument, I would like to state that I have nothing against towns; I am writing this purely because I live in the country and so I am therefore naturally biased (as well as being very argumentative).

Anyway, the first point I wish to make is that towns and cities have nowhere near as much character as small country villages. This is mainly because all the houses on some streets are all exactly the same! Countryside villages are pretty in the sense that they are filled with old English flowers and beautiful old stone houses.

Secondly, towns and cities are outrageously polluted. The air is full of petrol fumes and goodness knows how many chemicals that are constantly emerging from factory chimneys, which could be very harmful to the swarming

crowds below. The skyline is also polluted. Polluted with monstrous-looking blocks of flats and sky-scrapers, that is!

Furthermore, towns and cities have double the amount of crime there is in the countryside. Some people might say that towns have more police officers, so it's safer than living in the countryside, but even though the towns have more police officers, there is still more crime.

My final argument is that all the traffic in towns and cities only causes grief for many people waiting for buses that come late, or people getting in trouble with their partners for being late for some sort of meeting, and all because of traffic. The town centres are all swarming with motorists beeping their horns in impatient anger.

Personally, I would prefer to live in the countryside any day of the week, as there are too many health risks and problems for me to be happy living in a town or city.

By Olivia Burton, aged 10
West Burton CofE Primary School

 YORKSHIRE AND HUMBERSIDE WINNER

50

Town versus Country

There are good and bad things about living in villages, towns and cities. The view we have about them depends on many things. Whether we are young or old, have a car or not, whether we prefer peace and quiet to noise and bustle. Some people prefer to live in a busy town. They want to be surrounded by people and things to do, so they overlook all the bad things. Other people prefer a slower, quieter pace of life where it is easier to get to know people. Cities have crime, poverty and pollution but they are also places full of interest with museums, libraries and many historic buildings.

Most people value the English countryside. The sense of relaxation and good feeling they get out of enjoying the countryside and being able to "get away from it all" makes a real difference to people's quality of life. Fresh air and peace and quiet are some of the things people gain from the country. Most people value it whether they visit it or not. The countryside offers natural open space, unspoilt coasts and woodlands with opportunities for seeing wildlife and safe places for children to play. These are all the things that people consider important. Despite today's wide choice of leisure opportunities, people still enjoy the simple pleasures that come from contact with the countryside, such as walking, bird watching and cycling.

Nevertheless, people who live in the countryside can often feel isolated and lonely. A car is essential as there are very few bus routes, so it can be very difficult to get around. For old people it is especially difficult. Going to school, shopping and visiting

family and friends almost always involves a car journey. People who live in the countryside are more exposed to the weather. There is always the danger of being flooded, snowed in or having no electricity. There have also recently been the terrible problems caused by foot and mouth. All of these things can often make living in the countryside difficult.

Unlike the countryside, the city centre has lots of important buildings: libraries, museums, art galleries, hospitals and many beautiful old buildings. As well as these there are police stations, cinemas, bowling alleys and many different kinds of eating places. All of these things make life interesting and a lot easier for people. Shopping centres are now designed to provide a pleasant place to spend a whole day – eating places, cinemas, shops and amusements all under the same roof. However, many people are moving away from the city centre because of pollution, litter, traffic and parking problems as well as the fear of crime. They are all in search of a more peaceful, quiet lifestyle, with fresh air and green fields. Many more houses are needed to be built because of the growth in population, divorce and people living longer than ever before.

Having considered both the good and bad points about living in the town and the country I have decided that I would prefer to live in the town. This is because there are more local amenities. I think if I lived in the countryside I would feel lonely and isolated. It would be more difficult to do all the things I like to do such as visiting friends and family, going out to eat, visiting the library and going to the cinema. I like the countryside because of the fresh air, the open space and the peace and quiet. It is good to know that it is there whenever I want to visit it. However, I prefer to live in the town because there is more choice of things to do and people to see.

By Emma Woods, aged 10
Broomfields Junior School

NORTH WEST WINNER
NATIONAL WINNER

STORY

Jacqueline Wilson wrote…

I ran out of school and charged across the playground. I made for the school gates — but they were locked. I rattled them desperately, looking over my shoulder. I couldn't wait. I clawed my way over, one leg up, then the other. For a few dizzying seconds I was balanced at the very top. Then my shoe slipped and I fell forwards.

I landed on my hands and knees on the pavement. It knocked the breath out of me. I sat up gingerly, tears stinging my eyes. I held my hands up. They were both bleeding. I remembered long ago making palm prints in the nursery class with scarlet poster paint. I so wished I was back in that cosy world of yellow dough and plastic tea-sets and stories about hungry caterpillars.

I had no time to crouch there crying. I had to get away. I picked myself up, wincing at the pain in my knees. They were bleeding too, and speckled with gravel. I staggered up the road and round the corner. I ran and ran, not knowing where to go.

I went past house after house, all with their doors shut, their windows closed, their gardens guarded by little fences. A woman was unstrapping her baby from its buggy, her shopping bags tumbled by her ankles. The baby was wailing loudly, as pink as a prawn. I had this mad idea that I might run up to the woman and say "I'll carry your shopping indoors, okay? I can make a cup of tea too, I know how. Please let me stay with you. Just keep me safe."

INTRODUCING THE STORIES

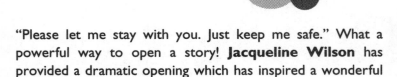

"Please let me stay with you. Just keep me safe." What a powerful way to open a story! **Jacqueline Wilson** has provided a dramatic opening which has inspired a wonderful range of writing.

Horror is the key to **Hannah Wisdish's** terrifying tale, which contrasts happy memories of school with present terrors to send shivers down our spines. **Ruth Taunton** explores compassion for others as a saving force in her evocative story of someone on the run.

Niral Panchal uses his story as an opportunity to discuss prejudice and the danger of judging others too readily as well as to outline the civilian casualties of war. His final line is a call to all readers to think carefully about their actions. **Samuel Gomez** vividly describes the heroic Ghost Catcher, who saves the school from a troublesome haunting, and the tricky ghost headmaster who runs away to haunt "for the rest of his death".

Emily Dixon explores prejudice and bullying in her dramatic story*. Her love for her mother is overriding – but is not enough to bring about a happy ending. We are left wondering – worrying about – what has happened and what the future holds. **Chris Sievwright's** spooky story grips us until the end, with its scary hooded figures and dream-like chase sequence. His final twist is surprising yet still dark – why have his so-called friends caused him to be lying in hospital?

Ashley Chin uses a bloody plot to explore guilt and friendship. In a bleak finale, the narrator realises that their only chance of happiness has been missed. The power of light comes to the rescue in **Meddy Barraball's** nightmarish vision, but the relief is only temporary before the tormentors return.

Benjamin Evans' amateur detective triumphs in his heroic story of criminal teachers and old-fashioned sleuth work. We hope his hero, Joe, will go on to be a detective of international fame. **Amy Manning** uses an initially scary ghost story to give us a heartwarming celebration of family love and reunion.

Bullying once again provides the background to **Laura Pudsey's** work, which gives us a realistic vision of the effect of bullying* on a child when they feel there is no one to turn to.

Horror... happiness... guilt... freedom... love... all these subjects and many more fill these powerful pieces of writing which show so clearly the talents of our winning storytellers.

*For information on bullying, see page 112.

Wild Memories

Of course, I knew that the woman wouldn't take me in; I had my own parents anyway. For a few minutes my mind wandered back to what had happened.

My dad had got a job in America and after two years there, we were now back for a holiday. When my mum and dad had gone out shopping this morning I sneaked back to my old school so I could recall some happy memories. To my surprise, I knew the directions quite well. But when I got there I didn't think I was in the right place. There were huge signs saying DANGER and KEEP OUT by the gate. Where were the flowers in the garden?

It seemed so dismal and lonely. Eaten up with curiosity, I found a hole in the fence and crept through. First I wandered into the main hall. Oh what memories I had there.

My first memory was when I had my Infant Nativity Play and I was so nervous that I fell off the stage. There was the time when I won the School Cross Country Championships. I can still remember my parents sitting there clapping away. They were so proud of me then. So was I. I stood up to move into another room when something struck me. I was sure the door leading to the Lunch-box Room had been closed. Oh well.

I walked into the Science Lab, one of my favourite places at school. We were very lucky to get a laboratory especially for Science as not many primary schools get them. I can still remember the day when the school was presented with loads of Science equipment like sets of scales, bottles for Chemistry and bags of colourful powders and liquids. I could never forget the Chemistry lesson I had when I turned my hair purple! As I wandered out to find my reception class I stopped. I thought I saw the scales move. How very strange. Quickly, I ran into my reception classroom. This was definitely my favourite class because of its cosy carpet and teddy bears on the curtains.

The memory of my first day at school is one I shall never forget. I had been looking forward to it for months but when I set eyes on the Year Sixes charging round I started bawling. Mum had had to bribe me with all sorts of things to make me let go of her hand. When I finally did get into the class I stopped crying almost at once and busied myself with some Lego.

Suddenly, the cobwebs by the door blew against the wall, making it look like old, worn-out lace. An icy chill blew softly into my face. Surprisingly, I felt a bit scared. I ran out. I paused to see where I was. I was terrified now. Everywhere I went it felt like someone was following me. The hairs on the back of my neck were standing straight up on end. Instinctively I ran into the Head's office. I always remember how kind and helpful Mr Clarke was, always ready to give advice. I leapt inside and slammed the door shut. Instantly, it became deathly quiet. Just then, something brushed against my leg.

As I stooped down to see what it was I noticed that it was a page torn from a newspaper. I turned it over and was horrified to read:

OAKWOOD PRIMARY CLOSES AFTER HEAD'S SUSPICIOUS DEATH

A door banged. The wind howled wildly. It's him. He's here. He's coming. I was petrified. I ran about madly trying to get out. It felt like he was grabbing at my ankles, dragging me down. Mist everywhere. Cobwebs blowing in my face. I saw the door. I was out.

So that's my story and I still haven't found my mum and dad. Now I'm out in the happy sunshine, the scariness of the school doesn't seem real any more. I wonder what mum'll say – there she is!

I'll never forget today. Dad says he doesn't believe in ghosts but I think there *was* something in there today, do you?

By Hannah Wisdish, aged 9
Duffield Meadows Primary School

 EAST MIDLANDS WINNER

GUILTY!

But I knew I wouldn't be safe. Not here, not in this town. I was as sure about that as I was sure that the filthy acrid smoke pouring out of the school was my fault. I hadn't meant it. I'd just had to have a fag, to prove to Johnny and the boys that I was just as tough as them. But I'd blown it. I'd set fire to the school.

The dancing flames mocked me. The screaming voices scourged me. The towering black smoke choked me.

I fled. I had to get away, get rid of that gruesome picture that I had caused. But the evil pillar of smoke chased me, seeming to twist into grotesque faces that laughed at me. I could maybe get a lawyer, argue that it wasn't my fault ... but it was no use. I knew I could not force myself to plead innocent when I knew I was guilty. I had no choice. I had to escape.

I ran on to the harbour (for I live in Great Yarmouth), with a large ferry all set to go off to France! I put on an extra burst of speed and just managed to scramble on board before the mooring rope fell limp.

I collapsed on the spare ropes and contemplated my situation. I was safe. I watched the black cloud of smoke bob into the distance. Yet it was not the only thing drifting away. My family, my friends, my life were left on that shore. The chubby cheeky boy that was Mike Johnson no longer existed here. It stabbed my heart. I was nothing, in a seemingly endless, cruel world.

I was jolted out of my thoughts by voices. I hurried round the deck and quickly crawled through a hatch to find myself in a parking lot. The sleek cars looked like slumbering beasts, ready to wake up and screech towards me ...! I was letting my imagination run away with me. I shook myself, and searched for somewhere to hide.

I was just looking for any cargo holds along one of the walls when I heard a noise. It was a sort of sad little whine, and it appeared to be coming from a bulky Landrover. I cautiously crept over to it, and peered through the dark window. I was horrified by what I saw.

A golden labrador gazed mournfully back at me. Its matted dirty coat was full of bare patches, and below its pleading stare an empty rib cage was displayed.

The poor creature whimpered and pawed at the window. I knew at once it was begging: begging for food, begging for warmth, begging for love.

I instantly felt I had to tell someone about her (for once she turned her back on me to pace up and down I knew it was a she) but it would blow my cover. I had to escape to France, for if I was found out I would be sent straight back to England, to face the law, to face my guilt.

On the other hand, I already had the sin of burning down the school, and if I ran off, this dog's life would add to my guilt. I knew I had to do it. I would face my fault.

I ran up the stairs, strangely enlightened by my choice. I felt a great weight lifted off my shoulders. I knew that I would be punished, and the punishment would take away my guilt. I whooped and cheered. I sprinted out onto the deck, and felt the wind whip my face, before I bumped straight into the Captain.

"What do you want?" he snapped acidly.
"Well, sir," I mumbled, "There's a dog locked in a car down below, she looks in pretty bad condition, and I thought you might, you might ..."
"Jan!" he barked to a nearby stewardess, "Go and see if what this boy says is true."

So there my story ends. Of course they found out who I was, and the minute they let the passengers off in France they sailed me back home. It wasn't as bad as I'd thought. It turned out the over-enthusiastic cookery class had accidentally started the fire, and everyone thought I was dead. Nobody was hurt anyway. I was allowed to keep the dog, which I called Jan, after the friendly, chatty stewardess. Everything was cleared up. Apart from one thing – I'll never talk to Johnny and his gang ever again!

By Ruth Taunton, aged 10
Milton CofE Primary School

EAST OF ENGLAND WINNER

The Cannibal

Before I could ask the nice lady to let me into her house, I felt a heavy, cold hand land on my shoulder. I froze, my heart raced even faster and a million thoughts ran through my head. I knew it was Mr Walimasa, our caretaker.

He was the most frightening person on this planet. He was as black as the winter night. He only had one eye. In the other eye socket was nothing but a gaping hole. His face was covered in the ugliest scars you ever saw. On his left arm was a clamp instead of a hand. Worse still, he never spoke or smiled. He just walked around the school.

There were hundreds of stories about how he came to look the way he did and why he never communicated. The one that came to my head was that he was from an African cannibal tribe who eat kids. "I've really had it now," I thought. "I don't want to die," I kept telling myself. "I haven't told my parents how much I love them." I was petrified. If I hadn't been silly I wouldn't have been kept behind after school.

He could see I was trembling. I bravely looked up at him. He grabbed hold of my hand with his metal claw, and placed a key into my hand. He looked at me gently.

I smiled back in between the panting and I let out a sigh of relief.

"Why were you running away so fast?" asked Mr Walimasa

in a broad African accent. "You dropped your key as you ran out of school. I was running after you to give it back."

"I ... I ... I ... was scared!" I stammered from the shock of hearing him speak.

"Scared of me?" he asked, concerned.

"Only because of what the children have been saying," I blurted out. "They have been saying that you are from an African cannibal tribe who eats children. So I was scared you might eat me."

"Ha! Ha! Ha! Ha! Ha!" Mr Walimasa threw his head back and laughed. He shook his head, still laughing. "No! No! I am a vegetarian. I don't eat children," he reassured me. "Why, why do they say this? Is it because of the way I look?" he asked.

"I think so," I said hesitantly, now not sure how I was feeling.

"Come," he said. He sat me down on a nearby bench and started telling me a story.

"Many, many years ago, I lived in Somalia with my mother Tusa, dad Jomato and older sister Kizi. When I was five years old, my mother got very sick so the family had to travel by road in our jeep to Nairobi for treatment. The journey would take at least a week so my mother packed plenty of food supplies and blankets.

"The road was very bumpy and dusty and the journey seemed endless but for our mother we had to make this trip. We were into the third night of our journey when something unimaginable happened. Just as my father rode the jeep over what seemed to be a huge rock, an almighty fireball emerged from the jeep together with a horrendous

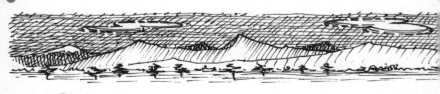

blast. My father had driven the jeep straight over a landmine in the darkness of the night.

"Locals from the nearby villages rushed to our aid, but unfortunately my mother Tusa, my father Jomato and Kizi my sister were all killed instantly and horrifically. I was thrown out of the jeep with the explosion and landed on some large rocks. That is how I lost my right eye. These scars you see on my face are also injuries from the rocks."

My stomach was beginning to churn. I was beginning to feel so differently about our caretaker. I felt awful for all the bad things that had been said about him. "What about your arm?" I asked, concerned.

"That came off with the explosion. That is why I have this," he said, holding up his arm.

"I was in terrible shock. I couldn't speak for months on end. The doctor who we were on our way to see for my mother decided to bring me to London. I have lived here since then but I'll never forget that nightmare. When I close my eyes I still picture it."

Tears streamed down Mr Walimasa's face. I found myself giving him a hug as I thought hard about the most important lesson I had learnt today and I hadn't learnt it in school.

By Niral Panchal, aged 9
Dairy Meadow Nursery and Primary School

LONDON WINNER
NATIONAL WINNER

67

The Ghost Catcher

Just keep me safe. I finally realised the boys were ghosts. My body started to shake and I was frightened. The boys looked normal but when I was nudging a boy my arm went through him. I thought it was a haunted school – all the teachers and boys were ghosts!

The school was made of old stone and had missing tiles and cracked pots. The playground had rotten fences, no grass, ruined swings and slides and old bent gates. The inside had broken glass and terrible food and books with no covers and torn pages. It was scary.

I thought the lady wouldn't believe me. So I dashed home to tell mum and dad that the school was full of ghosts. Dad rushed to the phone and dialled quickly. He phoned the ghost catcher and gave directions to the boarding school.

Damian Dean the ghost catcher wore big black boots and a green wetsuit. He had a helmet with a light and rubber gloves. He wore shoulder guards to protect himself. They were black and orange. They had a Nike logo on them. In his garage he owned a black van with a vacuum cleaner inside. He used it for catching ghosts.

I was hiding behind a big wall when I saw a van pull up. Next I saw another van with "Reinforcements" on the side in red letters. The ghost catcher had a knife. He unlocked the gates and rushed into the school.

The ghost catcher was walking around, not making a sound. He had his ghost hoover with him. It was black and red with big wheels. He hid behind a door and sucked the children up when they walked past. Suddenly one of the teachers got sucked up and the rest went through the wall. The teachers and the headmaster started a fight about which way to go. The ghost catcher was going to his van when he saw all the ghosts fighting. He grabbed his hoover and sucked them up but the headmaster realised and ran away to Chicago Boarding School, where he haunted for the rest of his death.

By Samuel Gomez, aged 10
Ridgeway Primary School

AWARDS FOR IMPROVEMENT JOINT WINNER

69

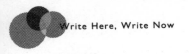

Escape!

But I was too late. The woman had dragged her overgrown prawn into her smart town house and the Asda bags had been hauled in. So I sprinted, terrified, past tiny cottages and tall town houses, until my scuffed school shoes caught on a sharp, protruding rock. In one terrifying second I was hurled forward, soaring; until with a sickening thud I hit the gravel. Tears stung my eyes and hate was written all over my mind as I charged down Dillon Street. The jeering and mocking still echoed eerily in my sweating head, and I knew I had to run further. I suppose I'm rambling again, like Mum...

It all started off as a perfectly normal Circle Time – usually my favourite time of the school week. So here I go. Nosy Nelly (my teacher Miss Neliba really) started rambling on about "Family Lives" (how amazing), just giving me time for a nap. I was just about to doze off when Nelly lowered her voice dramatically and whispered "Disabilities". I was juddered awake suddenly, sweat trickled down my face and I wobbled uncertainly on my chair. How I hate Nosy Nelly. She once again did her famous "Nebbie" and whispered "I wonder... has anyone got a friend like this?" I didn't expect anyone to put their hand up. But to my utter shock Belle Dawson's hand shot up, her posh charm bracelets dangling so everyone could see the little flashy diamonds. You could plainly see the shock on Nelly's wrinkly old face, but being the nosy nebber she is, she mused "And who is this poor pet, Belle?"

Belle was my all-time best friend (yeah, right), the sort who says, "So you're my friend – you're my slave". Anyway, Belle gave a smug little smile and a posh little flick of her ponytail and replied, "Well, she's got a rare disease and she can't walk or talk. She's Kiara Lambert's mum (at the mention of my name my eyes widened) and she should be..." The words "taken away" echoed unspoken as I flew at Belle, stuffed my tie in her mouth and flung her into the maths cupboard, where kilogram and gram weights thudded on her big fat head. I could hear Nelly screaming, but I was glad really.

So here I was, in the middle of town, with no idea what to do. My knee was still spouting blood, so I grabbed my blazer belt and bound it tightly. Before I knew it, tears were flooding over my eyes and screams erupted from my mouth. Blinded and screaming, I stumbled onto the A72, where a stocky bus driver asked, "You all right, love?" I didn't realise everyone was staring, transfixed by this figure of pity. So I gabbled, "Take me as far as you go, please – I've got £5, look!" The driver replied, "Alright love, here's some choccy, just sit at the back." I staggered to a leather seat, but I threw the chocolate out of the window. I must have dozed off because...

... I was awoken by a broad Cockney accent yelling "Off, me maties, off!" I sprinted up then sank to the ground. I was in London. Finding my breath I cried to the driver, "There's been a mistake! Take me back!" But the driver just shook his head and shooed me off. Howling, I ran to Thames Train Station and flung myself into the nearest carriage. The journey was never ending, so with the strain I curled up, when a crunch echoed beneath me. In horror, I pulled out a crumpled medicine packet marked "Fluoxide". Suddenly my heart started pounding.

Mum! She needed these by 4 o'clock! With the shock I fainted dead on the lavish silk chairs. Hours passed by and I didn't stir until the train juddered to an uncomfortable halt. I threw myself off and sprinted down Tallsend Lane. At my tiny cottage I flung open the door and raced up to Mum's room.

"Mum, I'm he..." I trailed off, because the room was empty. I was worried. I was scared. Mum was gone.

By Emily Dixon, aged 9
Ashley Primary School

NORTH EAST WINNER
NATIONAL RUNNER-UP

"You can Run but you Can't Hide"

I glanced over my shoulder again. There they were: three tall hooded figures surrounded by mist, all dressed in black, towering tall above me. I started running again, passing houses and houses, all locked up and black inside. Then I saw doors opening and demons, pumpkin-headed monsters, vampires and  everything scary that you can think of appearing from inside the houses. The streets started seething with noise and commotion.

I once again looked over my shoulder and saw the three misty, hooded figures gaining on me, but now I could see them properly. They had three long, wrinkly fingers with claws like diamonds, as sharp as blades, literally stuck on the ends of their fingers.

I hid behind a garden fence, but they found me. I kept on running, wishing it was all a nightmare. I pinched myself. "Ow!" That hurt. It was definitely not a nightmare.

Dogs barked madly as I started to sprint, past Mr Dodd's Joke Shop, up Moor Lane Avenue, past my best friend's house and into the park. The swings creaked and swung on

their own, the slide had a face, the monkey bars were twisting and turning and in the trees some big yellow eyes stared at me through the topmost branches. "You can run but you can't hide!" three cold voices said from behind me, which sounded strangely familiar.

The wind was a howling monster, screaming in the night, the moon was a ghostly ship sailing in the sky, and still the monsters kept pursuing me. I tried to lose them by weaving through the trees but they kept following me. I climbed a wall (climbing is my speciality). Only my three best friends John, Chris and Ben could climb as well and as fast as me, but these three figures were speeding up the wall behind me.

I ran down a small back street and noticed that now my leg was covered in blood, soaking my trousers. I looked up and saw that I was trapped. A large house was in front of me and two large brick walls towered high above me to either side. It was a dead end. I tried to grip on to the left sidewall and climb but not even I could manage to climb a wall ten times higher than me and that had no grip whatsoever.

I screamed as loud as I could scream but nobody could hear me. My scream was just a small mouse squeak compared to all the noise and commotion happening behind the house. The monsters were only about ten metres behind me now. I tried desperately to climb but I just couldn't. It was dusk now and becoming very dark. I could only just make out the monsters behind me now. I was petrified. I shouted out to them, "Leave me alone! What did I ever do? Do you hear me? Leave me alone!" They just kept coming closer and I was shaking madly. I could barely move.

I fell to the ground and tried to retreat to the wall of the house. I tried to get back up, but the hooded figures held me down and started lashing out at me. I backed away, still on the floor. I used all my strength to get back onto my feet and then lashed out at the nearest beast. I missed and fell flat on my face. I was bleeding madly and I felt as if my nose was broken. I had gravel in my knees and elbows. I lay down and decided to give up.

I woke up, lying in hospital, my mum and dad standing beside me, my three best friends standing outside my room with black robes in their hands. My mum gave me a parcel and I opened it. It contained a wolf's mask.

"Since it was Halloween last night, I thought you might be wanting this," Mum said.

"Thanks, Mum, but..."

"But what?"

"It doesn't matter," I answered.

By Chris Sievwright, aged 9
Bollin Primary School

   NORTH WEST WINNER

Not for the Faint-Hearted

There was nothing I could do now. I needed somewhere to go. I had no escape from school because of the killer. He was in my school as a visitor. He was only there to get near me. At lunch, he pulled out of his bag a large steak knife but before he could do anything with it, I ran. But if I went back to my foster parents, they would just send me back to the social services again, where I was bullied. They never liked me in the first place. I expect they were paid to have me for a short while. So they would still get to keep the money. They first took me in five years ago. I still remember my mum. But I don't remember anything about my dad.

All I could do now was find somewhere to hide and clean up my cuts. But this neighbourhood was evil. No-one here would do that for me. They were all weird and completely mad! So I just sat in the dark corner of a garage. The killer was after me. It had started with strange phone calls. Then letters written with lamb's blood saying YOU = GONE FOREVER. Now he was here. The person who wrote it was here to get me and me only. It was because I hurt his only child.

It started off as a game. Everyone joined in and it got extremely rough. The game was beside the train track. I fell into this boy and he rolled down the bank onto the track. His trainer lace got tangled in the track and he desperately tugged in a vain attempt to escape. I watched from the top of the bank, motionless. The poor boy, Mikey, was still struggling when suddenly a buzzing noise started. I listened, paralysed, and knew that a train was making its way towards Mikey. He realised what I already knew and when the train was visible in the distance, he started undoing his whole trainer. Mikey wasn't quick enough, though. That was the last I saw of him.

Eerie brightness was shining though the skylight. The cobwebs were easy to see now. The silence was overpowering. I was scared, truly petrified.

"AAAARRRGGGHHHHHHHHHH" I screamed as the garage door opened. But it was only the house owner.

"Who's in...?" the man enquired. Then his eyes bulged in surprise as he staggered forward and collapsed a few metres in front of me with a steak knife in his back. As I stared in disbelief, I was aware of something familiar about the man now lying dead at my feet. What was that smell? It reminded me of something long forgotten from my childhood, before I went to stay with my foster parents. The killer was behind him. As he walked forward, I didn't know what to do next. As he stepped slowly, I could envisage my own death approaching.

"You don't know the meaning of pain, do you?" laughed the killer madly. I closed my eyes and nearly fainted from fear! There was a small click, the sound of which I recognised as the safety catch of a gun being released. The killer was going to shoot me. I opened my eyes, hoping for a miracle to happen, and it did. The gun was not pointed at me, nor was it even in the killer's hands! The gun was that of a police officer who had been trained to deal with this situation.

I wasn't going to die. I was still alive ... but how did the police get here so soon? Well, that was their daily patrol of the streets. I was lucky. Lucky enough to still be alive. The killer was locked up for life. (Serves him right!) But I felt guilty about the house owner's death. I read about it in the local newspaper. I thought it would be decent to go to the funeral. So I went to the local church where the funeral was held. As I listened to the vicar's voice, I remembered all the bad things that had happened to me. The man's name was Andrew. I had learnt that from reading the newspaper. He was a father, of a girl called Louise. She was only eight, the same age as me ... I fell down on my hands and knees, exhausted with emotion. Tears were blurring my sight. I realised that the poor girl was ... was me!

By Ashley Chin, aged 10
Stone Cross School

 SOUTH EAST WINNER

Curse of Darkness

But the lady said "No" and started laughing and suddenly the lady slowly started changing into one of them. I was shaking and scared so I decided to run. I ran as fast as I could.

Everywhere I went I kept seeing one of them. I was out of breath. I thought this was the end for me. I kept seeing their terrible wings and their bodies were in the shape of a giant dragonfly. I couldn't see their faces because they were covered with darkness. Eventually they caught me. I didn't know what to do, so I screamed and shouted, "What do you want from me?" They didn't say anything back; they just gave me a strange rat with a burning tail. They told me to eat it or they would kill me. I had no choice but to eat the smelly, disgusting rat. It tasted awful.

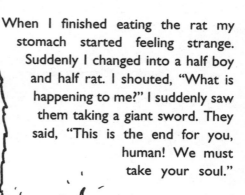

When I finished eating the rat my stomach started feeling strange. Suddenly I changed into a half boy and half rat. I shouted, "What is happening to me?" I suddenly saw them taking a giant sword. They said, "This is the end for you, human! We must take your soul."

They suddenly stabbed me in my left arm, but the strangest thing happened. I wasn't bleeding but I did feel a terrible pain deep in my arm. "I wish this was a bad nightmare," I said.

They were still coming for me. They moved closer and closer and suddenly a beam of light came. It was as bright as the sun. The light said, "Wherever there is darkness there will be light."

"I've got it!" I said, "All I need is light." So I took two stones and squeezed them together and shook them until a fire came and they suddenly started melting. Eventually they vanished out of existence. "Yes!" I said, "My curse and my nightmare are finally over!" Suddenly I turned back into a boy. I suddenly found myself in my bedroom. I said, "It was all just a nightmare and I'm glad it's all over now," but just then I heard their terrible voices.

They were coming back.

By Meddy Barraball, aged 10
New Christ Church CofE Primary School

AWARDS FOR IMPROVEMENT JOINT WINNER

Gangster Trouble

I decided better of it and sped on past, hoping she wouldn't see the bloody state I was in. I came to the local park and sprawled along the ground behind a large bush. I puffed and panted for quite a time, still scared about whether I was still being chased.

I'm Joe, a boy of thirteen and being educated at Midstream Comprehensive on the edge of York. As I found out on Tuesday, wanting to be a detective can be very dangerous. It started when my teacher was checking my work after the end of school. Everyone else had left. The night before I had heard about gangsters in my school on the news! You can tell I was watching out. While my teacher was supposedly looking for something in her cupboard, I saw her out of the corner of my eye speaking into a walkie-talkie. I was astounded but it didn't take me long to work out what to do. As I ran out of the door at full pelt I could hear my teacher saying, "Where are you going, Joe? We haven't finished," to "Come back, boy. You won't get away from us."

As I bashed open the nearest door other voices were zooming down the corridor.

And that is where I started, running across the playground.

And that is where I started.

*   *   *

The next morning in class our teacher was away and so were some others. It didn't take an international detective to work out that probably most of the teachers that were away may have been mixed up in my evening affair.

After taking the register to the secretary, I was passing the headteacher's office when I heard the head and the deputy talking in annoyed but hushed voices: "The money — all of it's gone ... and those important CDs." That was certainly a find! After I heard this I decided to sneak out to the school that night.

At about 1:15 am I sneaked out of the house. Fortunately it was not a long way to my school but the night was dark and it wasn't enjoyable. Eventually I came to the gates. Of course they were locked but it didn't take me long to find a hole in the fence. As soon as I stepped through I spotted lights on in a caravan classroom. I froze. I could hear mutterings inside so I clambered up to the window. Four people were sitting round a table. On the table was — even more exciting — a large bag of what could only be cash and about 20 CDs! I also noticed that there was a door right by the table. I had a plan.

The next few minutes were crucial. I banged open the door and rushed in. The gangsters stood up quickly and started to shout. I sped to the table, snatched up the money and software and raced back out of the door, rolling down the steps in the process. I could hear gun shots as I picked myself up.

Once again I was sprinting round the school, running away from the same robbers. As the gate came in sight I made a running jump at the gate. Bad idea. I crashed to the ground. I saw one of the gang run up behind me and he picked me up sharply. He was a great help. I climbed up onto his shoulders and with one more leap I was up and over and running as fast as I could towards the High Street. Tearing round the corner I finally reached the police station. Fortunately there was a policeman in there and after I told him my story, taking in deep breaths after every sentence, he telephoned a bigger police station in York.

"It's all right now, sonny. I've sent the police to the school," he said in the usual jolly voice.

The next morning dawned bright and the robbers were now behind bars. My parents had been woken the night before and told everything, much to their annoyance. Who knows ... maybe there will be another adventure some day for Joe the detective!

By Benjamin Evans, aged 10
Grove Junior School

SOUTH WEST WINNER

The Ghost Baby

I couldn't. I was too scared. I just wanted to wake up and think that it was all a strange dream. I suddenly felt cold, wet drops rolling slowly down my face. I was crying again.

The lady saw me and asked me why I was crying and why I was out there all alone.

I couldn't speak. It felt like my lips were sewn tightly together.

She invited me in. I hadn't the faintest idea who she was but I went in anyway. "What's your name?" she asked in a firm voice. I struggled but I finally got a word out: "N... N... Nicki," I stuttered. "Why are you crying?" she replied. I had a thought that she was a kidnapper and if I didn't tell her she would take me off to some mangy old fallen-down hut or shed, and tie me up then leave me there for the rest of my life.

So I told her everything, but not quite in detail.

"My mom, well my foster mom, had cancer for a long time, until now.

"I was at school when the office received a phone call. It was for me. I wasn't expecting anything serious, but it was the nurse. He told me that my foster mom was dead. For a moment I didn't understand the word *dead* and then I realised that it meant that my foster mom wasn't around any more. I turned round. Everyone was looking at me. I didn't know what to do, just start crying or go back and sit down as if nothing had happened.

"I chose a different option. I asked the teacher if I could go to the toilet, but when I got downstairs I ran onto the playground and climbed over the gate. I didn't know where to go but I kept on running and now I'm here."

The lady suggested for me to go back to school. "NO!" I screamed. The lady told me to calm down. It was very hard but I did it.

"Now, my name is Mrs Mead but you may call me by my first name, Sophie," the lady declared. "That's funny – my last name is Mead," I sniffed.

Sophie let me off that night and let me sleep there.

The house seemed to be very old, but I could swear it was haunted. I was about to go to sleep when I heard a scream. The baby was next to me but when I looked the baby was fast asleep.

Anyway, it felt like Sophie was part of my family ... but how could she be? My dad was dead and my mom was too young when she had me to look after me. I don't even know if I have any cousins.

All of a sudden I heard the same scream as I heard last night. I jumped up and saw a baby floating in mid air. I screamed and Sophie came rushing in. "What on Earth is the matter?" she asked.

"I ... I saw a baby floating in thin air!" I shouted. Sophie told me that she needed to tell me something. "Yes?" I replied.

"I am your mother, but before you say anything I need to tell you a little story.

"When I was young I had you but I was too young to look after you so I got you fostered.

"Ever since then I've lived here but, every night a ghost baby keeps screaming and when I look at it, it looks exactly the same as you did when you were a baby. Ever since then it's been haunting me."

I ran up to my real mom and hugged her, tears rolling down my eyes once more. I slept there again that night, and every night after, and guess what – there was no more ghost baby.

I live with my real mom now, and the baby she had is my half-sister Megan. I'm so happy to live with my mom and that is the only thing that matters.

By Amy Manning, aged 10
Westfield Primary School

WEST MIDLANDS WINNER

The Bullies

I stood there for a moment, staring at the lady. I didn't know what to do. I opened the little gate, walked up to the woman, cleared my throat and said in a nervous tone, "Can I help you?" The woman jumped in surprise and turned round to look at me. There was a moment's silence, and then the baby began to yell, louder and louder. I said in a shaky voice, "I can make you a cup of tea?" The woman looked down at me and said, in a very puzzled voice, "Why aren't you at school?" I suddenly froze. I tried desperately to think of a lie. I opened my mouth to reply, but nothing came out but a squeak. I tried again and finally said, "I'm not at school because we've got the afternoon off."

"Then why don't you go home?" asked the woman, looking rather puzzled. I suddenly froze again because that thought hadn't struck me. "I didn't go home because my mum's working night shift and I haven't got a key," I replied in a shaky voice. "Do any of your aunties or uncles live near?" the woman asked, giving me a look as if to say, "Well, that's stupid of your mum to leave you with no key and nobody to look after you."

Suddenly I felt something creeping over my hands and down my legs. I looked at my hands. I remembered the blood. I had all these questions buzzing round and round my head, like what if the woman saw the blood? And what would the woman do to me if she saw the blood? The woman did see the blood, just when I was hiding my hands. She looked shocked but then said in a much friendlier tone, "Do you want

to come inside and dab some cold water on your hands?" But I couldn't take any chances. I ran up to the gate, opened it, slammed it shut and ran off down Church Avenue.

My head was now starting to sweat. I suddenly stopped. I was now on Monastery Avenue. I started to walk. I walked past nine houses till I finally got to number 30. Home. I tiptoed up the drive, ever so quietly, and I slid through to the garden. My trousers were ripped and my jumper was torn. I ran to where I knew I would be safe for now. I put one foot on the tree and started to climb. I got to the very top, and there, nestled in the branches was my sanctuary, my tree house. This was perfect. It would be my secret hiding place.

I opened the door, went inside and slumped into a comfy-looking beanie chair. I quickly shot out my hand to look at my watch; it was only quarter past 3. I sat there in silence, not knowing what to do. Suddenly I heard somebody knocking loudly at the back door of the house. I opened the door of the tree house and peered round. I nearly fainted, because there in front of my mum, talking to her, was Mrs Couch, my head teacher. I heard her say, "I'm so sorry to interrupt you, but your daughter Laura has run out of school."

"When was this?" asked my mum, looking concerned. "Why would she run away from school?"

"There seems to be no reason," replied Mrs Couch.

My heart was in my mouth. How could I explain how unhappy I was at school? How could I tell my mum and Mrs Couch that I was being bullied by her favourite star pupils? I felt so ashamed. Even my teacher didn't like me. Even *he* bullied me. I had to think of something and I had to think of it quick. I didn't want to speak to my teachers; I didn't even want to speak to my mum. All I wanted was to feel safe. Safe like I felt with my grandma. Safe like I felt in hospital when I had my appendix out.

It suddenly struck me. If I were to have an accident, just a small accident like breaking a leg, I wouldn't have to go to school. But was I brave enough? I slowly went outside. I crept along the highest branch, shivering with fear. I looked down: it seemed such a long way. There were butterflies in my stomach. I felt sick. I closed my eyes and stepped off the branch ...

By Laura Pudsey, aged 9
Priory Lane Junior School

   YORKSHIRE AND HUMBERSIDE WINNER

JOURNALISM

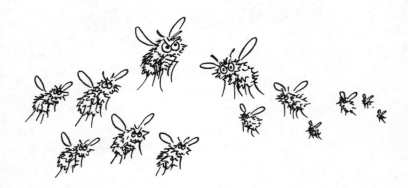

Lizo Mzimba wrote...

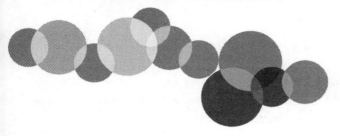

There are lots of important principles to remember when you're writing a report. Most articles should have most, or all, of the following bits of information – what happened, where it happened, who it happened to, how it happened and why it happened.

You should also always remember that you're aiming to make people interested enough to want to keep reading. So, in your opening sentences, try and get across the excitement or importance of what went on in the incident you're describing.

And in the rest of the article, do your best to make sure that it's not just a dull description. If appropriate, you could include short quotes from people who were there, or describe why what happened was so unusual.

Most importantly, the finished article, as well as being informative about an incident, should do its very best to make the person reading it feel as though they were actually there when it happened.

So **now it's your turn** and the headline for your report is INCIDENT AT LOCAL SCHOOL. You can change the headline if you want when you've written your piece – but make sure it's interesting enough to make me want to read your report!

INTRODUCING THE JOURNALISM

Lizo Mzimba's headline – INCIDENT AT LOCAL SCHOOL – inspired a wide range of subjects, from the familiar to the bizarre. The winning entries were written as newspaper articles or TV reports. All are precise in tone and arresting in content, with some great headlines!

Forest Town Primary put together a carefully edited and dramatic account of an escaped horse. Interviews with parents and teachers give their article a sense of realism and offer a variety of opinions. The theme of bullying is tackled once again, this time by **Hexham Middle School** in their hard-hitting TV report about a tragic suicide, supported by a vital helpline*.

Some humour creeps into **Peckover Primary's** report of a mystery bug – who can fail to smile at the thought of teachers covered in "large itchy spots"? – affecting the wonderfully named staff at a primary school. **Highfield Junior School's** entry uses carefully crafted newspaper language and is precisely edited to tell their story of killer bees efficiently yet in very informative detail.

A flood at **St Winefride's Catholic Primary School** provides a dramatic subject for this newspaper report, which makes us aware of the devastating effect it has on the school through interviews, lists of the damage and strong sub-headings. A TV report by **Glusburn Community Primary School** conjures up an hilarious image of fighting teachers – then surprises us with a twist in the ending.

TWO TREES TERRORISE! is a gripping headline that draws us immediately into **Kilmersdon CofE Primary School's** report, while natural forces feature again in **St Mark's CofE Primary's** article about a malicious "wild wind".

Finally, fantasy and realism mix in a gripping report by **Birch Copse Primary School,** which features David Beckham, an escaped panther and some searching interviews.

We can only hope that all our writers will go on to be journalists. Their styles, approaches and instincts for good stories are impressive and varied while their attention to detail is gripping.

* For information on bullying, see page 112.

FOREST TOWN NEWS 20p

FOREST TOWN HAS A VISITOR

On Monday 13th May a local school experienced dramatic events when it was invaded by a horse. Children at school were shocked and scared as their lessons were disrupted by a horse running through the school.

The horse, a plain white shire horse, escaped from the zoo and terrorised children as it galloped from class to class.

One of the students, Simon, aged 10, was in hospital suffering with a broken arm and bruises after the horse kicked him.

Mr Henderson, the zoo's director, last night spoke about his guilt over the incident. "I am very worried about this happening again. I will make the cages stronger."

As parents collected their children from school we asked them for their thoughts about the escaped horse. "We are very upset that the children got scared and hurt."

The staff hope that Simon will be back in the new year.

By David Bleby, Jake Henderson, Sam Pearson and Christopher Smith, aged 9 and 10
Forest Town Primary and Nursery School

EAST MIDLANDS WINNERS

School News

Tom H:
Tom R: Hello, and welcome to School News.

Tom H: I'm Tom Hacking.

Tom R: And I'm Thomas Renwick.

Tom H: The latest on the bullied boy at Bad Boy School is:

Tom R: After many attempts by witnesses to stop him, he jumped off a cliff.

Tom H: Simon Thomas really liked a girl, which made bullies want to bully him.

Tom R: Last night, at approximately 9.37 pm, Simon Thomas jumped off the end of John O'Groats and died from horrific injuries.

Tom H: Witnesses could only watch as Simon Thomas plunged to his death last night. We have a report from the scene.

Bobby I: Hello, I'm Bobby Innes reporting from the end of John O'Groats. Many people have gathered here to drop flowers in memory of Simon Thomas. Police cannot comprehend what would make an intelligent boy jump off the cliff. The parents of Simon Thomas have not yet arrived at John O'Groats but are on their way at this very moment. They will be obviously extremely upset by this terrible tragedy. Bobby Innes, School News Tonight.

Tom R: His parents blamed John Florence, Frederick Mark, Sarah Carrick and Claire Smith – the bullies.

Tom H: The parents, Susan Thomas and Kyle Thomas, hope to launch a court case against the bullies, hoping to get them privately prosecuted.

Tom R: We haven't had any more news on the court case. Obviously we'll give you any updates as soon as we get them.

Tom H: Thank you and good night.

Tom R: If you have any concerns about bullying please call our helpline. Calls are free.

By Nathan Bell, Tom Hacking, Bobby Innes, Christian Jervis, Greg Jones and Thomas Renwick, aged 9 and 10
Hexham Middle School

NORTH EAST WINNERS

MYSTERY BUG EMPTIES SCHOOL

The head teacher of a local primary school was very stressed this week when he had to teach over one hundred children unaided, due to a mystery bug which emptied the school.

Mr Sales, of Peckdown Primary, did not think it was unusual when two teachers phoned sick on Monday morning. Unable to get cover teachers, he took both classes himself. "It was extremely hard. Mrs Hand and Mrs Tight are rarely ill."

However, on Tuesday two more teachers went sick, leaving the reception pupils with no teachers. Mrs Bow and Mrs Biro were now infected with the mystery bug, which causes nausea, dizziness and large itchy spots to appear all over the face. At the end of the day Mr Sales and his remaining staff were shattered. "I have contacted supply teachers and they were afraid to come in case they caught the mystery bug. The school has had some advice from the Government. So far there haven't been any complaints." This suspicious bug only seems to infect the teachers.

Six-year-old Katrina Clarckson, a pupil at Peckdown, commented: "Mrs Biro was really sick all over her new shoes, she didn't like it and I cried." Mrs Clarckson, Katrina's mother, told us, "I can't believe that my six-year-old daughter has been taught by a Year Six pupil. On top of this, a teacher who was ill was still at school with the outrageous bug. I am thinking of removing my child from Peckdown School."

The bug continued to sweep through the school, and the two remaining teachers, Mrs Tick and Mrs Britain, looked exhausted by the end of the Wednesday.

As they were unable to return because the bug had taken them over, the school was closed down. Scientists still have no explanation why this bug is infecting adults.

It is hoped that the school will be opened by Monday. But Lydia Green (a Year Six pupil) said that she would be quite happy to look after the infants if worst comes to worst.

By Katrina Brooker, Lydia Gutteridge, Alice Henderson, Kristie Newman
and Emma Prendergast, aged 9 and 10
Peckover Primary School

EAST OF ENGLAND WINNERS

KILLER BEES INVADE SCHOOL

Editor: James Ashworth
Reporter: Laurence Sanders
Additional reporting: Oliver Barkwith

A HEADTEACHER was nearly trampled to death in the panic yesterday when a swarm of deadly bees invaded a school.

Peter Jones, 27, collapsed to the ground as his colleagues at Highfield Junior School, Bromley, fled.

At least six pupils were taken to hospital for treatment, after being stung by the bees.

Later the bees were identified as the species *Bombus Horribilis*, which can kill on occasions, but luckily the stings were too premature to do much harm.

In a muffled voice because of his bandages, Mr Jones said, "It was a very narrow escape for everyone, especially me, because most of the teachers had stiletto heels on."

It was noon when the first bee was spotted by pupil Cameron Sanders, eight. He had walked into the toilet to wash his hands when he noticed the insect flying around. He thought nothing of it and carried on washing his hands. Cameron walked over to the dryer and started to dry his hands. It was then that something out of the ordinary happened. Hundreds of bees started flying out of the dryer.

Master Sanders bolted out of the toilet and slammed the door, before noticing the insects squeezing through the keyhole.

Cameron rushed off to the staffroom and beat upon the door. It was opened by Miss Budd, a year 5 teacher. He explained the problem and then pulled her out into the corridor to show her.

When she saw them she gave a scream and told the other teachers to have a look. There was a mad rush for the door and it was then that the near-tragedy happened.

Mr Jones, who had just come back from a meeting, opened the door onto chaos. The teachers rushed out over him, crushing him to within an inch of his life beneath their feet.

The bees then made their way down the corridor, stinging six pupils doing errands. They flew off down the road and have not been seen since.

Pest control operatives were called in to investigate the dryer. When it was prised open a nest was discovered. Part of it was sent off to a laboratory in America to be analysed. We are still awaiting the outcome.

By James Ashworth, Oliver Barkwith and Laurence Sanders, aged 9 and 10
Highfield Junior School

WATERLOGGED ST WINEFRIDE'S!

St Winefride's Catholic Primary School on the Wirral was flooded on 8th May, 2001.

The flood occurred because the ballcock valve didn't turn the water supply off, so after a number of days it was overflowing and flooded the school. Mrs Owens, the caretaker, was the first to find out about the flood. As she opened the door and stepped into the school she was terribly shocked. She telephoned the headmistress to explain.

We spoke to the headmistress of St Winefride's, Mrs Brown, about how she reacted when she heard about the flood.

"The corridor, the ceilings, the electricity room and everything in it were ruined by the flood, as well as the playschool. We had a number of parents helping to wash and clean materials from the school. £13,000 worth of equipment was damaged. However, the money came back in insurance."

The children of St Winefride's got one day off school. The headteacher had to

put a sign on the gate, reading NO SCHOOL TODAY – MAJOR FLOOD.

Class 4 was destroyed by the flood. Mrs Henry, the teacher, told us all about it.

"I was horrified when I found out about the flood. I was worried about everything in the school.

"We swept all the water from the electricity room and threw all the carpets out."

Mrs Henry also said that the reception class came out the worst because they had just had new carpets fitted before the flood, and then they had to get new ones again.

Teachers wading in wellies

All the teachers of St Winefride's were wading

around Key Stage 1 in wellies with buckets full of water.

Clearing up

The books in Key Stage 1 were probably the worst problem, because most of them were ruined. Books were scattered around the infant playground, trying to dry off.

There was also string hung from one wall to another, acting as washing lines for other books. Some of the books weren't as fortunate as others, because as the teachers picked them up, they were torn apart or ripped.

In the flood the cloths in the priest's case were dyed red from the velvet lining the case. One of the members of the Parents' Association, Anthea Wright, had to take them home and wash and clean them until they were white again.

All the equipment in the electric room – the photocopier, the audio equipment, the television and one computer – had to be disposed of because the water went through gaps in the covers, and they had to be replaced.

We asked some children at the school how they felt about the flood. "It was absolutely amazing!" ... "I couldn't believe it – a day off school!"... "I had to feel sorry for the teachers. They had to do all the hard work."

Although the flood was a terribly bad experience for the school it turned out quite well. The school got a lot of new equipment, and also the Year Six pupils were relaxed, for they were studying hard in school. However, some pupils who weren't working so well got lower marks.

This year's students might not do as well because they worked non-stop and got rather stressed.

The flood was a truly terrible incident for St Winefride's, and although the children got the day off school, it was a hard day for the teachers, the PA and the cleaners.

By Frances Dee, Tessa Herzog, Martha Kieran, Frances Massie, Hannah Wilkie and Lowri Williams, aged 10
St Winefride's Catholic Primary School

NORTH WEST WINNERS

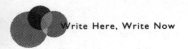
TEACHER SHOCK

Good evening and welcome to the news on March 13th. Earlier today, reports began to storm in from shocked onlookers of a horrendous fight between two primary school teachers. Mr Jones of Silverdale is obstinate to show that he only let fire because of Mr Tom's disgusting insults. Let's go over live to our primary correspondent who's there at the scene of the fight.

"Thank you, Kate. I'm standing here on the streets of Silverdale, where a fight has just taken place. Now to Brian, who is interviewing Mr Jones."

"So, Mr Jones, what do you have to say about Mr Tom's actions?"

"I think he is an insult to the human race and he should be banned from primary school teaching."

"Thank you, Brian. I am here in Glusburn school grounds where I am interviewing Mr Tom. What do you think of Mr Jones?"

"He's a pathetic, lying, sly man."

"Well, is he really that bad or are you exaggerating a bit?"

"I don't exaggerate!"

"A curious onlooker, who I interviewed earlier, told me that the corner of Mr Jones's black eye looked smudged. Back to the studio, thank you."

News just in from Silverdale confirms that the black eye of Mr Jones was indeed smudged. Over to our drama correspondent to find out what people think of this show.

"Thank you. Mr Tom, was the fight a set-up?"

"Of course it was. Mr Jones and I are good friends. I would never harm him. After interviewing a reception parent, though, I realised that not everyone was pleased. She said, 'I think it is a disgrace showing young children that kind of violence!'

"A young onlooker, on the other hand, said this: 'It was way cool'. "

"Back to the studio."

Well, a very different group of opinions. They had us all fooled there, didn't they? Whether you think it was funny, disgraceful or just plain good use of make-up, we can all agree on the fact that it was set up for the children's enjoyment. Well, that was certainly an eventful day in Silverdale.

And now for the weather.

By Emily Atkins, Thomas Collings, Nathan Pickles, Lauren Pitt, Robbie Purvis and Mary Savill, aged 10
Glusburn Community Primary School

YORKSHIRE AND HUMBERSIDE WINNERS

TWO TREES TERRORISE!

On Monday the 12th July 2002 at 12:20 at Kilmersdon School, the oak trees in the playground caused the school a lot of trouble. Not only did they fall down but they also hit a teacher and three students, causing significant damage.

The oak trees, which were planted approximately 200 years ago, fell on Kilmersdon School. The trees, which had been suffering from woodworm and were about to be treated for it, collapsed domino style onto two classrooms and part of the toilet block. No one was killed but it was a very close shave.

The trees hit two different classes and the recently modernised toilets. Unfortunately a teacher called Rosina Millians and three students named Liam Green, Sonya Reece and Amber Merchant were in the building and got hit by falling roof tiles but fortunately nobody was too seriously injured. Mrs Green, the mother of Liam Green, said, "Those trees shouldn't have been there in the first place." Amber Merchant's father, being a tree surgeon himself, had this to say: "Those trees should have been checked. The school doesn't deserve those trees. People just don't understand that trees need regular attention if you want them to stay strong and healthy."

Head teacher Steve Voake tells us, "I believe that this is a great loss to the school. Those oak trees were a big part of the school. Many a time I'd come out to find games of chase being played with the trees as 'base' and children just talking beneath them." But luckily these trees will not be forgotten as pupils are hoping to plant new trees soon. But will the local garden centre give the children some oak trees free or will they have to grow their own from the acorns on the ancient oak trees?

By Abigail Cousins, Kate Fenna and Mia Idiens, aged 9 and 10
Kilmersdon CofE Primary School

SOUTH WEST WINNERS
JOINT NATIONAL WINNERS

Doulwood Express

50p

WILD WIND TRAPS BOY'S THUMB

Yesterday at Doulwood school, a wild wind made a heavy window close on Nigel's thumb.

Crying and screaming Nigel, aged 10, was taken to hospital for stitches.

Mr Williams, the art teacher, had to scoop out Nigel's thumb from the window. Mr Williams said, "It was not very nice at all." The head teacher said, "It was a terrible accident."

The school phoned for an ambulance. It took 10 minutes to get there. Nigel's thumb end was hanging off. He was crying really badly after that. He was brave, though, when he had his stitches.

It was a shame that this happened to Nigel, because this was his first day at Doulwood school!

By Uroosa Ahmed, Rummana Awan, Rebecca Cavagin and Shahbaz Hussain, aged 9
St Mark's CofE Primary School

WEST MIDLANDS WINNERS

PANTHER COMES FOR LESSONS – SPOTTED BY BECKHAM

You have joined us at the six o'clock news with Georgie Kilford and Emma Rawding. Here is the main headline for tonight:

PANTHER COMES FOR LESSONS – SPOTTED BY BECKHAM

Last night a panther broke into Birch Copse Primary School. David Beckham was driving past to see his niece when he saw a hole in the fence which made him suspicious. The panther escaped from Marwell Zoo. We think that it could have smelt the leftovers in the school kitchen.

The panther broke a hole in the fence, then the panther smashed the window of the girls' toilets. He chased Mr Mullen (the caretaker) who was changing the paper towels. He got badly hurt. An ambulance came and took Mr Mullen to hospital. Then the panther ate the leftovers in the kitchen. It escaped from Marwell Zoo because the zoo keeper was feeding it and left the cage door open. We are now passing you over to Daniel Schofield.

"This is Daniel Schofield reporting live at old Trafford.

I'm here with David Beckham. Is it all right if we ask you some questions?"

"Yeah, sure."

"What did you think when you saw the panther?"

"My first thought was that someone was hurt."

"What was your reaction?"

"I was scared and didn't know what to do."

"Were you a bit suspicious before you saw the panther and was there any evidence that something was going on?"

"Yes I was, because there was a hole in the fence."

"Why were you coming to Birch Copse?"

"I was coming to the school to coach the football team."

"Did you think it was capable of killing someone?"

"Yes, because it was huge and looked very fierce."

We are now passing you over to Jon McKenry.

"This is Jon McKenry reporting live at Marwell Zoo. I am here with the zoo keeper. Is it OK if I ask you some questions about the panther?"

"Yeah, that's fine."

"What were you doing while the panther escaped?"

"Getting food for the panther."

"How did the panther escape?"

"It jumped over the fence."

"When did you notice the panther was gone?"

"When I came back to give him his food."

"What are you going to do with the panther?"

"We are going to send him back to the wild."

"Do you think you will be sacked for letting the panther get loose?"

"I will probably get suspended for a year."

That's all for tonight. Join us next week for more news.

By Georgie Kilford, Jon McKenry, Emma Rawding and Daniel Schofield, aged 9 and 10
Birch Copse Primary School

SOUTH EAST WINNERS

Bullying – how to deal with it

These are some of the things you could do if you are being bullied yourself:

• Look them in the eye and tell them to stop.

• Get away from the situation as quickly as possible.

• Tell an adult, either a parent or member of the school staff, what has happened. If necessary, ask a friend to go with you. If you can, explain clearly what has happened, how often, who was involved, where it happened and whether anyone else saw what happened.

• Don't blame yourself for the situation.

• If you need more help, you could ring the free confidential helpline at **ChildLine** on 0800 1111. Your parent could complain to the school authorities or local education authority, or contact a free helpline at **Parentline Plus** (0808 800 2222).

• Above all, DON'T KEEP IT TO YOURSELF.

Now It's Your Turn!

Create your own piece of brilliant writing, using one of the fantastic starters from John Hegley, Terry Jones, Jacqueline Wilson or Lizo Mzimba.

_____

_____

_____

_____

_____

_____

_____

_____

_____

_____

_____

_____

_____

_____

_____

_____